POEMS EVERY CHILD SHOULD KNOW
in Cursive

A *D'Nealian Cursive* copywork book with Thirty-two original poems by various authors from <u>Poems Every Child Should Know</u>, Part I, edited by Mary E. Burt. Each lesson includes the original poem to read followed by the poem in D'Nealian cursive with practice lines for handwriting practice.

by Classical Charlotte Mason

Conditions and Terms of Use

This text was produced and distributed by Classical Charlotte Mason. The books which Classical Charlotte Mason republishes are in the public domain and are no longer protected by the original copyright. They may therefore be reproduced within the United States without paying a royalty to the author.

The text used to produce this version of the work, however, are the property of Classical Charlotte Mason and are subject to certain restrictions. These restrictions are imposed for the purpose of protecting the integrity of the work, for preventing plagiarism, and for helping to assure that compromised versions of the work are not widely disseminated.

You may not alter this text or try to pass off all or any part of it as your own work. You may not distribute copies of this text for commercial purposes. This his text is a complete and UNABRIDGED copy of the original document. However, typos, omissions, and other errors may have occurred during preparation, and Classical Charlotte Mason does not guarantee a perfectly reliable reproduction.

For permission to use Classical Charlotte Mason documents or images for commercial purposes, or more information about our collection of resources can be obtained by contacting us at Info@ClassicalCharlotteMason.com

Poems Every Child Shoud Know in Cursive

Poems and D'Nealian Cursive Copywork Book

Copyright © Classical Charlotte Mason 2021

Some rights reserved

ISBN: 978-1-952118-06-7

www.ClassicalCharlotteMason.com

How to Teach Copywork:

Copywork can seem simplistic. Give your child a sentence or two and have them copy it. It can also seem like busy work, but the benefits are great! Copywork is a simple introduction to handwriting, spelling, and composition. Have children copy only the best authors, with the best writing, and ideas to fill their growing minds.

When to begin copywork:

Once a child learns how to write their letters comfortably, they are ready to start simple copywork. Start with very short sentences and have them copy it, always in their best handwriting. It is important that they give their best effort. If you find them struggling, give them less to copy. In the beginning, it's okay if they only do a few words per sitting as long as it is in their best handwriting. You can gradually increase the length of the model as they become more and more comfortable. However, it is important to take their age into consideration. As they gain age and experience with copywork the quantity and quality of their work should improve.

Why copywork:

Copying models of good writing teaches children what good writing looks and sounds like, thereby improving their own writing. Many of the world greatest writers learned how to write through copywork. Benjamin Franklin would copy or outline essays and then try to recreate them on his own to see if he could write them better.

How to use this book:

Poems Every Child Should Know in Cursive, Part I, copywork book includes the original unabridged poems to be read prior the each copywork lesson. No need to purchase the book if you do not already own it. Read the passage, and in the child's best handwriting, copy the poem on the lines provided paying close attention to capitalization and punctuation. Every student does not have to complete each lesson in the book; or even an entire lesson in one day, depending on age and ability. Choose the original poems and copywork lessons that work best for your family, not all may be suitable. Schedule chosen lessons over one or more years as desired.

For additional resources please visit www.ClassicalCharlotteMason.com

a b c d e f g h i j k l m

n o p q r s t u v w x y z

A B C D E F G H I J

K L M N O P Q R S T

U V W X Y Z , ' . ?

1 2 3 4 5 6 7 8 9 10

TABLE OF CONTENT **PART I**

Lesson 1: Read the poem and complete the copywork that follows in your best handwriting.

The Arrow and the Song

I shot an arrow into the air,
It fell to earth, I knew not where;
For, so swiftly it flew, the sight
Could not follow it in its flight.
I breathed a song into the air,
It fell to earth, I knew not where;
For who has sight so keen and strong
That it can follow the flight of song?
Long, long afterward, in an oak
I found the arrow, still unbroke;
And the song, from beginning to end,
I found again in the heart of a friend.

-Henry W. Longfellow

The Arrow and the Song

I shot an arrow into the air,

It fell to earth, I knew not where;

For, so swiftly it flew, the sight

Lesson 2: Read the poem and complete the copywork that follows in your best handwriting.

The Babie
"Her face is like an angel's face,
I'm glad she has no wings."
Nae shoon to hide her tiny taes,
Nae stockin' on her feet;
Her supple ankles white as snaw,
Or early blossoms sweet.
Her simple dress o' sprinkled pink,
Her double, dimplit chin,
Her puckered lips, and baumy mou',
With na ane tooth within.
Her een sae like her mither's een,
Twa gentle, liquid things;
Her face is like an angel's face:
We're glad she has nae wings.
-Jeremiah Eames Rankin

The Babie

"Her face is like an angel's face,

I'm glad she has no wings."

Nae shoon to hide her tiny taes,

Nae stockin' on her feet;

Her supple ankles white as snaw,

Or early blossoms sweet.

Her simple dress o' sprinkled pink,

Her double, dimplit chin,

Her puckered lips, and baumy mou',

With na ane tooth within.

Her een sae like her mither's een,

Twa gentle, liquid things;

Her face is like an angel's face:

We're glad she has nae wings.

-Jeremiah Eames Rankin

Lesson 3: Read the poem and complete the copywork that follows in your best handwriting.

Let Dogs Delight to Bark and Bite
Let dogs delight to bark and bite,
For God hath made them so;
Let bears and lions growl and fight,
For 'tis their nature too.
But, children, you should never let
Such angry passions rise;
Your little hands were never made
To tear each other's eyes.
-Isaac Watts

Let Dogs Delight to Bark and Bite

Let dogs delight to bark and bite,

For God hath made them so;

Let bears and lions growl and fight,

For 'tis their nature too.

But, children, you should never let

Such angry passions rise;

Your little hands were never made

To tear each other's eyes.

-Isaac Watts

Lesson 4: Read the poem and complete the copywork that follows in your best handwriting.

Little Things
Little drops of water,
Little grains of sand,
Make the mighty ocean
And the pleasant land.
Thus the little minutes,
Humble though they be,
Make the mighty ages
Of eternity.
-Ebenezer Cobham Brewer

Little Things

Little drops of water,

Little grains of sand,

Make the mighty ocean

And the pleasant land.

Thus the little minutes,

_____
_____
_____

Humble though they be,

_____
_____
_____

Make the mighty ages

_____
_____
_____

Of eternity.

_____
_____
_____

-Ebenezer Cobham Brewer

_____
_____
_____

Lesson 5: Read the poem and complete the copywork that follows in your best handwriting.

He Prayeth Best
Farewell, farewell! but this I tell
To thee, thou Wedding-Guest!
He prayeth well who loveth well
Both man and bird and beast.
He prayeth best who loveth best
All things, both great and small:
For the dear God who loveth us,
He made and loveth all.
-Samuel T. Coleridge

He Prayeth Best

Farewell, farewell! but this I tell

To thee, thou Wedding-Guest!

He prayeth well who loveth well

Both man and bird and beast.

He prayeth best who loveth best

All things, both great and small:

For the dear God who loveth us,

He made and loveth all.

-Samuel T. Coleridge

Lesson 6: Read the poem and complete the copywork that follows in your best handwriting.

Twinkle, Twinkle, Little Star
Twinkle, twinkle, little star!
How I wonder what you are,
Up above the world so high,
Like a diamond in the sky.
When the glorious sun is set,
When the grass with dew is wet,
Then you show your little light,
Twinkle, twinkle all the night.
In the dark-blue sky you keep,
And often through my curtains peep,
For you never shut your eye,
Till the sun is in the sky.
As your bright and tiny spark
Guides the traveller in the dark,
Though I know not what you are,
Twinkle, twinkle, little star!
-Anonymous

Twinkle, Twinkle, Little Star.

Twinkle, twinkle, little star!

How I wonder what you are,

Up above the world so high,

Like a diamond in the sky.

When the glorious sun is set,

When the grass with dew is wet,

Then you show your little light,

Twinkle, twinkle all the night.

In the dark-blue sky you keep,

And often through my curtains peep,

For you never shut your eye,

Till the sun is in the sky.

As your bright and tiny spark

Guides the traveller in the dark,

Though I know not what you are,

Twinkle, twinkle, little star!

Lesson 8: Read the poem and complete the copywork that follows in your best handwriting.

The Days of the Month
Thirty days hath September,
April, June, and November;
February has twenty-eight alone.
All the rest have thirty-one,
Excepting leap-year—that's the time
When February's days are twenty-nine.
-An Old Song

The Days of the Month

Thirty days hath September,

April, June, and November;

February has twenty-eight alone.

All the rest have thirty-one,

Excepting leap-year—that's the time

When February's days are twenty-
nine.

-An Old Song

Lesson 9: Read the poem and complete the copywork that follows in your best handwriting.

True Royalty
There was never a Queen like Balkis,
From here to the wide world's end;
But Balkis talked to a butterfly
As you would talk to a friend.
There was never a King like Solomon,
Not since the world began;
But Solomon talked to a butterfly
As a man would talk to a man.
She was Queen of Sabaea—
And he was Asia's Lord—
But they both of 'em talked to butterflies
When they took their walks abroad.
Rudyard Kipling

True Royalty

There was never a Queen like Balkis,

From here to the wide world's end;

But Balkis talked to a butterfly

As you would talk to a friend.

There was never a King like Solomon,

Not since the world began;

But Solomon talked to a butterfly

As a man would talk to a man.

She was Queen of Sabaea—

And he was Asia's Lord—

But they both of 'em talked to
butterflies

When they took their walks abroad.

Rudyard Kipling

Lesson 10: Read the poem and complete the copywork that follows in your best handwriting.

Playing Robinson Crusoe
Pussy can sit by the fire and sing,
Pussy can climb a tree,
Or play with a silly old cork and string
To 'muse herself, not me.
But I like Binkie, my dog, because
He knows how to behave;
So, Binkie's the same as the First Friend was,
And I am the Man in the Cave.
Pussy will play Man-Friday till
It's time to wet her paw
And make her walk on the window-sill
(For the footprint Crusoe saw);
Then she fluffles her tail and mews,
And scratches and won't attend.
But Binkie will play whatever I choose,
And he is my true First Friend.
Pussy will rub my knees with her head,
Pretending she loves me hard;
But the very minute I go to my bed
Pussy runs out in the yard.
And there she stays till the morning light;
So I know it is only pretend;
But Binkie, he snores at my feet all night,
And he is my Firstest Friend!
Rudyard Kipling

Playing Robinson Crusoe

Pussy can sit by the fire and sing,

Pussy can climb a tree,

Or play with a silly old cork and
string

To 'muse herself, not me.

But I like Binkie, my dog, because

He knows how to behave;

So, Binkie's the same as the First
Friend was,

And I am the Man in the Cave.

Pussy will play Man-Friday till

It's time to wet her paw

And make her walk on the window-
sill

(For the footprint Crusoe saw);

Then she fluffles her tail and mews,

And scratches and won't attend.

But Binkie will play whatever I choose,

And he is my true First Friend.

Pussy will rub my knees with her head,

Pretending she loves me hard;

But the very minute I go to my bed

Pussy runs out in the yard.

And there she stays till the morning light;

So I know it is only pretend;

But Binkie, he snores at my feet all night,

And he is my Firstest Friend!

Rudyard Kipling

Lesson 11: Read the poem and complete the copywork that follows in your best handwriting.

My Shadow
I have a little shadow that goes in and out with me,
And what can be the use of him is more than I can see.
He is very, very like me from the heels up to the head;
And I see him jump before me, when I jump into my bed.
The funniest thing about him is the way he likes to grow—
Not at all like proper children, which is always very slow;
For he sometimes shoots up taller like an india-rubber ball,
And he sometimes gets so little that there's none of him at all.
He hasn't got a notion of how children ought to play,
And can only make a fool of me in every sort of way.
He stays so close beside me, he's a coward, you can see;
I'd think shame to stick to nursie as that shadow sticks to me!
One morning, very early, before the sun was up,
I rose and found the shining dew on every buttercup;
But my lazy little shadow, like an arrant sleepy-head,
Had stayed at home behind me and was fast asleep in bed.
Robert Louis Stevenson

My Shadow

I have a little shadow that goes in and out with me,

And what can be the use of him is
more than I can see.

He is very, very like me from the heels
up to the head;

And I see him jump before me, when
I jump into my bed.

The funniest thing about him is the
way he likes to grow—

Not at all like proper children, which is
always very slow;

For he sometimes shoots up taller like
an india-rubber ball,

And he sometimes gets so little that there's none of him at all.

He hasn't got a notion of how children ought to play,

And can only make a fool of me in every sort of way.

He stays so close beside me, he's a
coward, you can see;

I'd think shame to stick to nursie as
that shadow sticks to me!

One morning, very early, before the
sun was up,

I rose and found the shining dew on every buttercup;

But my lazy little shadow, like an arrant sleepy-head,

Had stayed at home behind me and was fast asleep in bed.

Robert Louis Stevenson

Lesson 12: Read the poem and complete the copywork that follows in your best handwriting.

Little White Lily
Little White Lily
Sat by a stone,
Drooping and waiting
Till the sun shone.
Little White Lily
Sunshine has fed;
Little White Lily
Is lifting her head.
Little White Lily
Said: "It is good
Little White Lily's
Clothing and food."
Little White Lily
Dressed like a bride!
Shining with whiteness,
And crownèd beside!
Little White Lily
Drooping with pain,
Waiting and waiting
For the wet rain.
Little White Lily
Holdeth her cup;
Rain is fast falling
And filling it up.
Little White Lily
Said: "Good again,
When I am thirsty
To have the nice rain.
Now I am stronger,
Now I am cool;
Heat cannot burn me,
My veins are so full."
Little White Lily
Smells very sweet;
On her head sunshine,
Rain at her feet.
Thanks to the sunshine,
Thanks to the rain,
Little White Lily
Is happy again.
-George Macdonald

Little White Lily

Little White Lily

Sat by a stone,

Drooping and waiting

Till the sun shone.

Little White Lily

Sunshine has fed;

41

Little White Lily

Is lifting her head.

Little White Lily

Said: "It is good

Little White Lily's

Clothing and food."

Little White Lily

Dressed like a bride!

Shining with whiteness,

And crownèd beside!

Little White Lily

Drooping with pain,

Waiting and waiting

For the wet rain.

Little White Lily

Holdeth her cup;

Rain is fast falling

And filling it up.

Little White Lily

Said: "Good again,

When I am thirsty

To have the nice rain.

Now I am stronger,

Now I am cool;

Heat cannot burn me,

My veins are so full."

Little White Lily

Smells very sweet;

On her head sunshine,

Rain at her feet.

Thanks to the sunshine,

Thanks to the rain,

Little White Lily

Is happy again.

-George Macdonald

Lesson 13: Read the poem and complete the copywork that follows in your best handwriting.

How the Leaves Came Down

"I'll tell you how the leaves came down,"
The great Tree to his children said:
"You're getting sleepy, Yellow and Brown,
Yes, very sleepy, little Red.
It is quite time to go to bed."
"Ah!" begged each silly, pouting leaf,
"Let us a little longer stay;
Dear Father Tree, behold our grief!
'Tis such a very pleasant day,
We do not want to go away."
So, for just one more merry day
To the great Tree the leaflets clung,
Frolicked and danced, and had their way,
Upon the autumn breezes swung,
Whispering all their sports among—
"Perhaps the great Tree will forget,
And let us stay until the spring,
If we all beg, and coax, and fret."
But the great Tree did no such thing;
He smiled to hear their whispering.
"Come, children, all to bed," he cried;
And ere the leaves could urge their prayer,
He shook his head, and far and wide,
Fluttering and rustling everywhere,
Down sped the leaflets through the air.
I saw them; on the ground they lay,
Golden and red, a huddled swarm,
Waiting till one from far away,
White bedclothes heaped upon her arm,
Should come to wrap them safe and warm.
The great bare Tree looked down and smiled.
"Good-night, dear little leaves," he said.
And from below each sleepy child
Replied, "Good-night," and murmured,
"It is so nice to go to bed!"
-Susan Coolidge

How the Leaves Came Down

"I'll tell you how the leaves came down,"

The great Tree to his children said:

"You're getting sleepy, Yellow and Brown,

Yes, very sleepy, little Red.

It is quite time to go to bed. "

"Ah!" begged each silly, pouting leaf,

"Let us a little longer stay;

Dear Father Tree, behold our grief!

'Tis such a very pleasant day,

We do not want to go away. "

So, for just one more merry day

To the great Tree the leaflets clung,

Frolicked and danced, and had their
way,

Upon the autumn breezes swung,

Whispering all their sports among—

"Perhaps the great Tree will forget,

And let us stay until the spring,

If we all beg, and coax, and fret."

But the great Tree did no such thing;

He smiled to hear their whispering.

"Come, children, all to bed," he cried;

And ere the leaves could urge their
prayer,

He shook his head, and far and wide,

Fluttering and rustling everywhere,

Down sped the leaflets through the air.

I saw them; on the ground they lay,

Golden and red, a huddled swarm,

Waiting till one from far away,

White bedclothes heaped upon her arm,

Should come to wrap them safe and warm.

The great bare Tree looked down and smiled.

"Good-night, dear little leaves," he said.

And from below each sleepy child

Replied, "Good-night," and murmured,

"It is so nice to go to bed!"

-Susan Coolidge

Lesson 14: Read the poem and complete the copywork that follows in your best handwriting.

Willie Winkie
Wee Willie Winkie rins through the town,
Up-stairs and doon-stairs, in his nicht-gown,
Tirlin' at the window, cryin' at the lock,
"Are the weans in their bed?—for it's now ten o'clock."
Hey, Willie Winkie! are ye comin' ben?
The cat's singin' gay thrums to the sleepin' hen,
The doug's speldered on the floor, and disna gie a cheep;
But here's a waukrife laddie that winna fa' asleep.
Onything but sleep, ye rogue! glow'rin' like the moon,
Rattlin' in an airn jug wi' an airn spoon,
Rumblin' tumblin' roun' about, crowin' like a cock,
Skirlin' like a kenna-what—wauknin' sleepin' folk.
Hey, Willie Winkie! the wean's in a creel!
Waumblin' aff a body's knee like a vera eel,
Ruggin' at the cat's lug, and ravellin' a' her thrums,—
Hey, Willie Winkie!—See, there he comes!
Wearie is the mither that has a storie wean,
A wee stumpie stoussie that canna rin his lane,
That has a battle aye wi' sleep before he'll close an ee;
But a kiss frae aff his rosy lips gies strength anew to me.
-William Miller

Willie Winkie

Wee Willie Winkie rins through the town,

55

Up-stairs and doon-stairs, in his nicht-gown,

Tirlin' at the window, cryin' at the lock,

"Are the weans in their bed?—for it's now ten o'clock."

Hey, Willie Winkie! are ye comin'
ben?

The cat's singin' gay thrums to the
sleepin' hen,

The doug's speldered on the floor, and
disna gie a cheep;

But here's a waukrife laddie that winna
fa' asleep.

Onything but sleep, ye rogue!
glow'rin' like the moon,

Rattlin' in an airn jug wi' an airn
spoon,

Rumblin' tumblin' roun' about,
crowin' like a cock,

Skirlin' like a kenna-what—
wauknin' sleepin' folk.

Hey, Willie Winkie! the wean's in a
creel!

Waumblin' aff a body's knee like a vera eel,

Ruggin' at the cat's lug, and ravellin' a' her thrums,—

Hey, Willie Winkie!—See, there he comes!

Wearie is the mither that has a storie wean,

A wee stumpie stoussie that canna rin his lane,

That has a battle aye wi' sleep before he'll close an ee;

But a kiss frae aff his rosy lips gies
strength anew to me.

-William Miller

Lesson 15: Read the poem and complete the copywork that follows in your best handwriting.

The Owl and the Pussy-Cat
The Owl and the Pussy-Cat went to sea
In a beautiful pea-green boat;
They took some honey, and plenty of money
Wrapped up in a five-pound note.
The Owl looked up to the moon above,
And sang to a small guitar,
"O lovely Pussy! O Pussy, my love!
What a beautiful Pussy you are,—
You are,
What a beautiful Pussy you are!"
Pussy said to the Owl, "You elegant fowl!
How wonderful sweet you sing!
Oh, let us be married,—too long we have tarried,—
But what shall we do for a ring?"
They sailed away for a year and a day
To the land where the Bong-tree grows,
And there in a wood a piggy-wig stood
With a ring in the end of his nose,—
His nose,
With a ring in the end of his nose.
"Dear Pig, are you willing to sell for one shilling
Your ring?" Said the piggy, "I will,"
So they took it away, and were married next day
By the turkey who lives on the hill.
They dined upon mince and slices of quince,
Which they ate with a runcible spoon,
And hand in hand on the edge of the sand
They danced by the light of the moon,—
The moon,
They danced by the light of the moon.
-Edward Lear

The Owl and the Pussy-Cat

The Owl and the Pussy-Cat went to sea

In a beautiful pea-green boat;

They took some honey, and plenty of money

Wrapped up in a five-pound note.

The Owl looked up to the moon above,

And sang to a small guitar,

"O lovely Pussy! O Pussy, my love!

What a beautiful Pussy you are,—

You are,

What a beautiful Pussy you are!"

Pussy said to the Owl, "You elegant fowl!

How wonderful sweet you sing!

Oh, let us be married,—too long we
have tarried,—

But what shall we do for a ring?"

They sailed away for a year and a day

To the land where the Bong-tree grows,

And there in a wood a piggy-wig stood

With a ring in the end of his nose, —

His nose,

With a ring in the end of his nose.

"Dear Pig, are you willing to sell for
one shilling

Your ring?" Said the piggy, "I will,"

So they took it away, and were
married next day

By the turkey who lives on the hill.

They dined upon mince and slices of
quince,

Which they ate with a runcible spoon,

And hand in hand on the edge of the sand

They danced by the light of the moon, —

The moon,

They danced by the light of the moon.

-Edward Lear

Lesson 16: Read the poem and complete the copywork that follows in your best handwriting.

Wynken, Blynken, and Nod
Wynken, Blynken, and Nod one night
Sailed off in a wooden shoe,—
Sailed on a river of crystal light
Into a sea of dew.
"Where are you going, and what do you wish?"
The old moon asked the three.
"We have come to fish for the herring-fish
That live in this beautiful sea;
Nets of silver and gold have we,"
Said Wynken,
Blynken,
And Nod.
The old moon laughed and sang a song,
As they rocked in the wooden shoe;
And the wind that sped them all night long
Ruffled the waves of dew;
The little stars were the herring-fish
That lived in the beautiful sea.
"Now cast your nets wherever you wish,—
Never afeard are we!"
So cried the stars to the fishermen three,
Wynken,
Blynken,
And Nod.
All night long their nets they threw
To the stars in the twinkling foam,—
Then down from the skies came the wooden shoe,
Bringing the fishermen home:
'Twas all so pretty a sail, it seemed
As if it could not be;
And some folk thought 'twas a dream they'd dreamed
Of sailing that beautiful sea;
But I shall name you the fishermen three:
Wynken,
Blynken,
And Nod.
Wynken and Blynken are two little eyes,
And Nod is a little head,
And the wooden shoe that sailed the skies
Is a wee one's trundle-bed;
So shut your eyes while Mother sings

Of wonderful sights that be,
And you shall see the beautiful things
As you rock on the misty sea
Where the old shoe rocked the fishermen three,
Wynken,
Blynken,
And Nod.
-Eugene Field

Wynken, Blynken, and Nod

Wynken, Blynken, and Nod one night

Sailed off in a wooden shoe,—

Sailed on a river of crystal light

Into a sea of dew.

"Where are you going, and what do
you wish?"

The old moon asked the three.

"We have come to fish for the herring-
fish

That live in this beautiful sea;

Nets of silver and gold have we, "

Said Wynken,

Blynken,

And Nod.

The old moon laughed and sang a
song,

As they rocked in the wooden shoe;

And the wind that sped them all night long

Ruffled the waves of dew;

The little stars were the herring-fish

That lived in the beautiful sea.

"Now cast your nets wherever you wish,—

Never afeard are we!"

So cried the stars to the fishermen three,

Wynken,

Blynken,

And Nod.

All night long their nets they threw

To the stars in the twinkling foam,—

Then down from the skies came the
wooden shoe,

Bringing the fishermen home:

'Twas all so pretty a sail, it seemed

As if it could not be;

And some folk thought 'twas a dream
they'd dreamed

Of sailing that beautiful sea;

But I shall name you the fishermen three:

Wynken,

Blynken,

And Nod.

Wynken and Blynken are two little eyes,

And Nod is a little head,

And the wooden shoe that sailed the skies

Is a wee one's trundle-bed;

So shut your eyes while Mother sings

Of wonderful sights that be,

And you shall see the beautiful things

As you rock on the misty sea

Where the old shoe rocked the fishermen
three,

Wynken,

Blynken,

And Nod.

-Eugene Field

Lesson 17: Read the poem and complete the copywork that follows in your best handwriting.

The Duel
The gingham dog and the calico cat
Side by side on the table sat;
'Twas half-past twelve, and (what do you think!)
Nor one nor t'other had slept a wink!
The old Dutch clock and the Chinese plate
Appeared to know as sure as fate
There was going to be a terrible spat.
(I wasn't there; I simply state
What was told to me by the Chinese plate!)
The gingham dog went "bow-wow-wow!"
And the calico cat replied "mee-ow!"
The air was littered, an hour or so,
With bits of gingham and calico,
While the old Dutch clock in the chimney-place
Up with its hands before its face,
For it always dreaded a family row!
(Now mind: I'm only telling you
What the old Dutch clock declares is true!)
The Chinese plate looked very blue,
And wailed, "Oh, dear! what shall we do!"
But the gingham dog and the calico cat
Wallowed this way and tumbled that,
Employing every tooth and claw
In the awfullest way you ever saw—
And, oh! how the gingham and calico flew!
(Don't fancy I exaggerate!
I got my views from the Chinese plate!)
Next morning where the two had sat
They found no trace of the dog or cat;
And some folks think unto this day
That burglars stole the pair away!
But the truth about the cat and the pup
Is this: They ate each other up!
Now what do you really think of that!
(The old Dutch clock it told me so,
And that is how I came to know.)
-Eugene Field

The Duel

The gingham dog and the calico cat

Side by side on the table sat;

'Twas half-past twelve, and (what do
you think!)

Nor one nor t'other had slept a wink!

The old Dutch clock and the Chinese
plate

Appeared to know as sure as fate

There was going to be a terrible spat.

(I wasn't there; I simply state

What was told to me by the Chinese
plate!)

The gingham dog went "bow-wow-wow!"

And the calico cat replied "mee-ow!"

The air was littered, an hour or so,

With bits of gingham and calico,

While the old Dutch clock in the chimney-place

Up with its hands before its face,

For it always dreaded a family row!

(Now mind: I'm only telling you

What the old Dutch clock declares is true!)

The Chinese plate looked very blue,

And wailed, "Oh, dear! what shall we do!"

But the gingham dog and the calico cat

Wallowed this way and tumbled that,

Employing every tooth and claw

In the awfullest way you ever saw—

And, oh! how the gingham and calico
flew!

(Don't fancy I exaggerate!

I got my views from the Chinese
plate!)

Next morning where the two had sat

They found no trace of the dog or cat;

And some folks think unto this day

That burglars stole the pair away!

But the truth about the cat and the pup

Is this: They ate each other up!

Now what do you really think of that!

(The old Dutch clock it told me so,

And that is how I came to know.)

- Eugene Field

Lesson 18: Read the poem and complete the copywork that follows in your best handwriting.

The Boy Who Never Told a Lie.
Once there was a little boy,
With curly hair and pleasant eye—
A boy who always told the truth,
And never, never told a lie.
And when he trotted off to school,
The children all about would cry,
"There goes the curly-headed boy—
The boy that never tells a lie."
And everybody loved him so,
Because he always told the truth,
That every day, as he grew up,
'Twas said, "There goes the honest youth."
And when the people that stood near
Would turn to ask the reason why,
The answer would be always this:
"Because he never tells a lie."
-Anonymous

The Boy Who Never Told a Lie.

Once there was a little boy,

With curly hair and pleasant eye—

A boy who always told the truth,

And never, never told a lie.

And when he trotted off to school,

The children all about would cry,

"There goes the curly-headed boy—

The boy that never tells a lie."

And everybody loved him so,

Because he always told the truth,

That every day, as he grew up,

'Twas said, "There goes the honest
youth."

And when the people that stood near

Would turn to ask the reason why,

The answer would be always this:

"Because he never tells a lie."

- Anonymous

Lesson 19: Read the poem and complete the copywork that follows in your best handwriting.

Love Between Brothers and Sisters
Whatever brawls disturb the street,
There should be peace at home;
Where sisters dwell and brothers meet,
Quarrels should never come.
Birds in their little nests agree;
And 'tis a shameful sight,
When children of one family
Fall out and chide and fight.
-Isaac Watts

Love Between Brothers and Sisters

Whatever brawls disturb the street,

There should be peace at home;

Where sisters dwell and brothers meet,

Quarrels should never come.

Birds in their little nests agree;

And 'tis a shameful sight,

When children of one family
Fall out and chide and fight.

-Isaac Watts

Lesson 20: Read the poem and complete the copywork that follows in your best handwriting.

The Bluebell of Scotland.
Oh where! and oh where! is your Highland laddie gone?
He's gone to fight the French for King George upon the throne;
And it's oh! in my heart how I wish him safe at home.
Oh where! and oh where! does your Highland laddie dwell?
He dwells in merry Scotland at the sign of the Bluebell;
And it's oh! in my heart that I love my laddie well.
-Anonymous

The Bluebell of Scotland

Oh where! and oh where! is your Highland laddie gone?

He's gone to fight the French for King George upon the throne;

And it's oh! in my heart how I wish
him safe at home.

Oh where! and oh where! does your
Highland laddie dwell?

He dwells in merry Scotland at the
sign of the Bluebell;

And it's oh! in my heart that I love
my laddie well.

- Anonymous

Lesson 21: Read the poem and complete the copywork that follows in your best handwriting.

If I Had But Two Little Wings
If I had but two little wings
And were a little feathery bird,
To you I'd fly, my dear!
But thoughts like these are idle things
And I stay here.
But in my sleep to you I fly:
I'm always with you in my sleep!
The world is all one's own.
And then one wakes, and where am I?
All, all alone.
-Samuel T. Coleridge

If I Had But Two Little Wings.

If I had but two little wings

And were a little feathery bird,

To you I'd fly, my dear!

But thoughts like these are idle things

And I stay here.

But in my sleep to you I fly:

I'm always with you in my sleep!

The world is all one's own.

And then one wakes, and where am I?

All, all alone.

-Samuel T. Coleridge

Lesson 22: Read the poem and complete the copywork that follows in your best handwriting.

A Farewell
My fairest child, I have no song to give you;
No lark could pipe to skies so dull and gray;
Yet, ere we part, one lesson I can leave you
For every day.
Be good, sweet maid, and let who will be clever;
Do noble things, not dream them all day long:
And so make life, death, and that vast forever
One grand, sweet song.
Charles Kingsley.

A Farewell

My fairest child, I have no song to give you;

No lark could pipe to skies so dull and
gray;

Yet, ere we part, one lesson I can leave
you

For every day.

Be good, sweet maid, and let who will
be clever;

Do noble things, not dream them all day long:

And so make life, death, and that vast forever

One grand, sweet song.

-Charles Kingsley

Lesson 23: Read the poem and complete the copywork that follows in your best handwriting.

Casabianca
The boy stood on the burning deck,
Whence all but him had fled;
The flame that lit the battle's wreck
Shone round him o'er the dead.
Yet beautiful and bright he stood,
As born to rule the storm;
A creature of heroic blood,
A proud though childlike form.
The flames rolled on—he would not go
Without his father's word;
That father, faint in death below,
His voice no longer heard.
He called aloud, "Say, father, say
If yet my task is done?"
He knew not that the chieftain lay
Unconscious of his son.
"Speak, father!" once again he cried,
"If I may yet be gone!"
And but the booming shots replied,
And fast the flames rolled on.
Upon his brow he felt their breath,
And in his waving hair;
And looked from that lone post of death
In still, yet brave despair.
And shouted but once more aloud
"My father! must I stay?"
While o'er him fast, through sail and shroud,
The wreathing fires made way.
They wrapt the ship in splendour wild,
They caught the flag on high,
And streamed above the gallant child
Like banners in the sky.
Then came a burst of thunder sound—
The boy—oh! where was he?
—Ask of the winds that far around
With fragments strew the sea;
With mast, and helm, and pennon fair.
That well had borne their part—
But the noblest thing that perished there
Was that young, faithful heart.
-Felicia Hemans

Casabianca

The boy stood on the burning deck,

Whence all but him had fled;

The flame that lit the battle's wreck

Shone round him o'er the dead.

Yet beautiful and bright he stood,

As born to rule the storm;

A creature of heroic blood,

A proud though childlike form.

The flames rolled on—he would not go

Without his father's word;

That father, faint in death below,

His voice no longer heard.

He called aloud, "Say, father, say

If yet my task is done?"

He knew not that the chieftain lay

Unconscious of his son.

"Speak, father!" once again he cried,

"If I may yet be gone!"

And but the booming shots replied,

And fast the flames rolled on.

Upon his brow he felt their breath,

And in his waving hair;

And looked from that lone post of death

In still, yet brave despair.

And shouted but once more aloud

"My father! must I stay?"

While o'er him fast, through sail and shroud,

shroud,

The wreathing fires made way.

They wrapt the ship in splendour wild,

They caught the flag on high,

And streamed above the gallant child

Like banners in the sky.

Then came a burst of thunder sound—

The boy—oh! where was he?

—Ask of the winds that far around

With fragments strew the sea;

With mast, and helm, and pennon fair.

That well had borne their part—

But the noblest thing that perished there

Was that young, faithful heart.

-Felicia Hemans

Lesson 24: Read the poem and complete the copywork that follows in your best handwriting.

The Captain's Daughter
We were crowded in the cabin,
Not a soul would dare to sleep,—
It was midnight on the waters,
And a storm was on the deep.
'Tis a fearful thing in winter
To be shattered by the blast,
And to hear the rattling trumpet
Thunder, "Cut away the mast!"
So we shuddered there in silence,—
For the stoutest held his breath,
While the hungry sea was roaring
And the breakers talked with Death.
As thus we sat in darkness,
Each one busy with his prayers,
"We are lost!" the captain shouted
As he staggered down the stairs.
But his little daughter whispered,
As she took his icy hand,
"Isn't God upon the ocean,
Just the same as on the land?"
Then we kissed the little maiden.
And we spoke in better cheer,
And we anchored safe in harbour
When the morn was shining clear.
-James T. Fields

The Captain's Daughter

We were crowded in the cabin,

Not a soul would dare to sleep,—

It was midnight on the waters,

And a storm was on the deep.

'Tis a fearful thing in winter

To be shattered by the blast,

And to hear the rattling trumpet

Thunder, "Cut away the mast!"

So we shuddered there in silence, —

For the stoutest held his breath,

While the hungry sea was roaring

And the breakers talked with Death.

As thus we sat in darkness,

Each one busy with his prayers,

"We are lost!" the captain shouted

As he staggered down the stairs.

But his little daughter whispered,

As she took his icy hand,

"Isn't God upon the ocean,

Just the same as on the land?"

Then we kissed the little maiden.

And we spoke in better cheer,

And we anchored safe in harbour

When the morn was shining clear.

-James T. Fields

Lesson 25: Read the poem and complete the copywork that follows in your best handwriting.

The Village Blacksmith
Under a spreading chestnut-tree
The village smithy stands;
The smith, a mighty man is he,
With large and sinewy hands,
And the muscles of his brawny arms
Are strong as iron bands.
His hair is crisp, and black, and long;
His face is like the tan;
His brow is wet with honest sweat,
He earns whate'er he can,
And looks the whole world in the face,
For he owes not any man.
Week in, week out, from morn till night,
You can hear his bellows blow;
You can hear him swing his heavy sledge,
With measured beat and slow,
Like a sexton ringing the village bell,
When the evening sun is low.
And children coming home from school
Look in at the open door;
They love to see the flaming forge,
And hear the bellows roar,
And catch the burning sparks that fly
Like chaff from a threshing-floor.
He goes on Sunday to the church,
And sits among his boys;
He hears the parson pray and preach,
He hears his daughter's voice
Singing in the village choir,
And it makes his heart rejoice.
It sounds to him like her mother's voice,
Singing in Paradise!
He needs must think of her once more,
How in the grave she lies;
And with his hard, rough hand he wipes
A tear out of his eyes.
Toiling,—rejoicing,—sorrowing,
Onward through life he goes;
Each morning sees some task begin,
Each evening sees it close;
Something attempted, something done,

Has earned a night's repose.
Thanks, thanks to thee, my worthy friend,
For the lesson thou hast taught!
Thus at the flaming forge of life
Our fortunes must be wrought;
Thus on its sounding anvil shaped
Each burning deed and thought.
-Henry W. Longfellow

The Village Blacksmith

Under a spreading chestnut-tree

The village smithy stands;

The smith, a mighty man is he,

With large and sinewy hands,

And the muscles of his brawny arms

Are strong as iron bands.

His hair is crisp, and black, and long;

His face is like the tan;

His brow is wet with honest sweat,

He earns whate'er he can,

And looks the whole world in the face,

For he owes not any man.

Week in, week out, from morn till night,

You can hear his bellows blow;

You can hear him swing his heavy sledge,

With measured beat and slow,

Like a sexton ringing the village bell,

When the evening sun is low.

And children coming home from
school

Look in at the open door;

They love to see the flaming forge,

And hear the bellows roar,

And catch the burning sparks that fly

Like chaff from a threshing-floor.

He goes on Sunday to the church,

And sits among his boys;

He hears the parson pray and preach,

He hears his daughter's voice

Singing in the village choir,

And it makes his heart rejoice.

It sounds to him like her mother's voice,

Singing in Paradise!

He needs must think of her once more,

How in the grave she lies;

And with his hard, rough hand he
wipes

A tear out of his eyes.

Toiling, — rejoicing, — sorrowing,

Onward through life he goes;

Each morning sees some task begin,

Each evening sees it close;

Something attempted, something done,

Has earned a night's repose.

Thanks, thanks to thee, my worthy friend,

For the lesson thou hast taught!

Thus at the flaming forge of life

Our fortunes must be wrought;

Thus on its sounding anvil shaped

Each burning deed and thought.

-Henry W. Longfellow

Lesson 26: Read the poem and complete the copywork that follows in your best handwriting.

Sweet and Low
Sweet and low, sweet and low,
Wind of the western sea,
Low, low, breathe and blow,
Wind of the western sea!
Over the rolling waters go,
Come from the dropping moon and blow,
Blow him again to me;
While my little one, while my pretty one sleeps.
Sleep and rest, sleep and rest,
Father will come to thee soon;
Rest, rest, on mother's breast,
Father will come to thee soon;
Father will come to his babe in the nest,
Silver sails all out of the west
Under the silver moon:
Sleep, my little one, sleep, my pretty one, sleep.
-Alfred Tennyson

Sweet and Low

Sweet and low, sweet and low,

Wind of the western sea,

Low, low, breathe and blow,

Wind of the western sea!

Over the rolling waters go,

Come from the dropping moon and blow,

Blow him again to me;

While my little one, while my pretty
one sleeps.

Sleep and rest, sleep and rest,

Father will come to thee soon;

Rest, rest, on mother's breast,

Father will come to thee soon;

Father will come to his babe in the nest,

nest,

Silver sails all out of the west

Under the silver moon:

Sleep, my little one, sleep, my pretty one, sleep.

- Alfred Tennyson

Lesson 27: Read the poem and complete the copywork that follows in your best handwriting.

The Violet
Down in a green and shady bed
A modest violet grew;
Its stalk was bent, it hung its head,
As if to hide from view.
And yet it was a lovely flower,
No colours bright and fair;
It might have graced a rosy bower,
Instead of hiding there.
Yet there it was content to bloom,
In modest tints arrayed;
And there diffused its sweet perfume,
Within the silent shade.
Then let me to the valley go,
This pretty flower to see;
That I may also learn to grow
In sweet humility.
-Jane Taylor

The Violet

Down in a green and shady bed

A modest violet grew;

Its stalk was bent, it hung its head,

As if to hide from view.

And yet it was a lovely flower,

No colours bright and fair;

It might have graced a rosy bower,

Instead of hiding there.

Yet there it was content to bloom,

In modest tints arrayed;

And there diffused its sweet perfume,

Within the silent shade.

Then let me to the valley go,

This pretty flower to see;

That I may also learn to grow

In sweet humility.

- Jane Taylor

Lesson 28: Read the poem and complete the copywork that follows in your best handwriting.

The Rainbow
My heart leaps up when I behold
A rainbow in the sky;
So was it when my life began,
So is it now I am a man,
So be it when I shall grow old,
Or let me die!
The child is father of the man;
And I could wish my days to be
Bound each to each by natural piety.
-William Wordsworth

The Rainbow

My heart leaps up when I behold

A rainbow in the sky;

So was it when my life began,

So is it now I am a man,

So be it when I shall grow old,

Or let me die!

The child is father of the man;

And I could wish my days to be

Bound each to each by natural piety.

-William Wordsworth.

Lesson 29: Read the poem and complete the copywork that follows in your best handwriting.

A Visit From St. Nicholas

'Twas the night before Christmas, when all through the house
Not a creature was stirring, not even a mouse;
The stockings were hung by the chimney with care,
In hopes that St. Nicholas soon would be there;
The children were nestled all snug in their beds,
While visions of sugar-plums danced in their heads;
And mamma in her 'kerchief, and I in my cap,
Had just settled our brains for a long winter's nap,
When out on the lawn there arose such a clatter,
I sprang from the bed to see what was the matter.
Away to the window I flew like a flash,
Tore open the shutters and threw up the sash.
The moon on the breast of the new-fallen snow
Gave the luster of mid-day to objects below,
When, what to my wondering eyes should appear,
But a miniature sleigh, and eight tiny reindeer.
With a little old driver, so lively and quick,
I knew in a moment it must be St. Nick.
More rapid than eagles his coursers they came,
And he whistled, and shouted, and called them by name:
"Now, Dasher! now, Dancer! now, Prancer and Vixen!
On, Comet! on, Cupid! on, Donder and Blitzen!
To the top of the porch! to the top of the wall!
Now dash away! dash away! dash away all!"
As dry leaves that before the wild hurricane fly,
When they meet with an obstacle, mount to the sky;
So up to the house-top the coursers they flew,
With the sleigh full of toys, and St. Nicholas, too.
And then, in a twinkling, I heard on the roof
The prancing and pawing of each little hoof.
As I drew in my head, and was turning around,
Down the chimney St. Nicholas came with a bound.
He was dressed all in fur, from his head to his foot,
And his clothes were all tarnished with ashes and soot;
A bundle of toys he had flung on his back,
And he looked like a peddler just opening his pack.
His eyes—how they twinkled! his dimples how merry!
His cheeks were like roses, his nose like a cherry!
His droll little mouth was drawn up like a bow,
And the beard of his chin was as white as the snow;
The stump of a pipe he held tight in his teeth,
And the smoke it encircled his head like a wreath;

He had a broad face and a little round belly,
That shook when he laughed, like a bowlful of jelly.
He was chubby and plump, a right jolly old elf,
And I laughed when I saw him, in spite of myself;
A wink of his eye and a twist of his head,
Soon gave me to know I had nothing to dread;
He spoke not a word, but went straight to his work,
And filled all the stockings; then turned with a jerk,
And laying his finger aside of his nose,
And giving a nod, up the chimney he rose;
He sprang to his sleigh, to his team gave a whistle,
And away they all flew like the down on a thistle.
But I heard him exclaim, ere he drove out of sight,
"Happy Christmas to all, and to all a good-night."
-Clement Clarke Moore

A Visit From St. Nicholas

'Twas the night before Christmas, when all through the house

Not a creature was stirring, not even a mouse;

The stockings were hung by the chimney with care,

In hopes that St. Nicholas soon would be there;

The children were nestled all snug in their beds,

While visions of sugar-plums danced in their heads;

And mamma in her 'kerchief, and I in my cap,

Had just settled our brains for a long winter's nap,

When out on the lawn there arose such a clatter,

I sprang from the bed to see what was the matter.

Away to the window I flew like a
flash,

Tore open the shutters and threw up the
sash.

The moon on the breast of the new-
fallen snow

Gave the luster of mid-day to objects below,

When, what to my wondering eyes should appear,

But a miniature sleigh, and eight tiny reindeer.

With a little old driver, so lively and quick,

I knew in a moment it must be St. Nick.

More rapid than eagles his coursers they came,

And he whistled, and shouted, and
called them by name:

"Now, Dasher! now, Dancer! now,
Prancer and Vixen!

On, Comet! on, Cupid! on, Donder
and Blitzen!

To the top of the porch! to the top of the
wall!

Now dash away! dash away! dash away
all!"

As dry leaves that before the wild
hurricane fly,

When they meet with an obstacle,
mount to the sky;

So up to the house-top the coursers they
flew,

With the sleigh full of toys, and St.
Nicholas, too.

And then, in a twinkling, I heard on
the roof

The prancing and pawing of each
little hoof.

As I drew in my head, and was
turning around,

Down the chimney St. Nicholas came
with a bound.

He was dressed all in fur, from his head
to his foot,

And his clothes were all tarnished with
ashes and soot;

A bundle of toys he had flung on his back,

And he looked like a peddler just opening his pack.

His eyes—how they twinkled! his dimples how merry!

His cheeks were like roses, his nose like a
cherry!

His droll little mouth was drawn up
like a bow,

And the beard of his chin was as white
as the snow;

The stump of a pipe he held tight in his
teeth,

And the smoke it encircled his head like
a wreath;

He had a broad face and a little round
belly,

That shook when he laughed, like a
bowlful of jelly.

He was chubby and plump, a right
jolly old elf,

And I laughed when I saw him, in
spite of myself;

A wink of his eye and a twist of his head,

Soon gave me to know I had nothing to dread;

He spoke not a word, but went straight to his work,

And filled all the stockings; then
turned with a jerk,

And laying his finger aside of his nose,

And giving a nod, up the chimney he
rose;

He sprang to his sleigh, to his team
gave a whistle,

And away they all flew like the down
on a thistle.

But I heard him exclaim, ere he drove
out of sight,

"Happy Christmas to all, and to all a
good-night."

-Clement Clarke Moore

Lesson 30: Read the poem and complete the copywork that follows in your best handwriting.

The Star-Spangled Banner

O! say, can you see, by the dawn's early light,
What so proudly we hailed at the twilight's last gleaming—
Whose broad stripes and bright stars, through the perilous fight,
O'er the ramparts we watched were so gallantly streaming!
And the rocket's red glare, the bombs bursting in air,
Gave proof through the night that our flag was still there;
O! say, does that star-spangled banner yet wave
O'er the land of the free, and the home of the brave?
On that shore dimly seen through the mists of the deep,
Where the foe's haughty host in dread silence reposes,
What is that which the breeze, o'er the towering steep,
As it fitfully blows, now conceals, now discloses?
Now it catches the gleam of the morning's first beam,
In full glory reflected now shines on the stream;
'Tis the star-spangled banner; O long may it wave
O'er the land of the free, and the home of the brave!
And where is that band who so vauntingly swore
That the havoc of war and the battle's confusion
A home and a country should leave us no more?
Their blood has washed out their foul footsteps, pollution.
No refuge could save the hireling and slave
From the terror of flight, or the gloom of the grave;
And the star-spangled banner in triumph doth wave
O'er the land of the free, and the home of the brave.
O! thus be it ever, when freemen shall stand
Between their loved homes and the war's desolation!
Blest with victory and peace, may the heav'n-rescued land
Praise the power that hath made and preserved us a nation.
Then conquer we must, for our cause it is just,
And this be our motto—"In God is our trust":
And the star-spangled banner in triumph shall wave
O'er the land of the free, and the home of the brave.
-Francis Scott Key

158

The Star-Spangled Banner

O! say, can you see, by the dawn's
early light,

What so proudly we hailed at the

twilight's last gleaming—

Whose broad stripes and bright stars,

through the perilous fight,

O'er the ramparts we watched were so gallantly streaming!

And the rocket's red glare, the bombs bursting in air,

Gave proof through the night that our flag was still there;

O! say, does that star-spangled banner
yet wave

O'er the land of the free, and the home
of the brave?

On that shore dimly seen through the
mists of the deep,

Where the foe's haughty host in dread silence reposes,

What is that which the breeze, o'er the towering steep,

As it fitfully blows, now conceals, now discloses?

Now it catches the gleam of the morning's first beam,

In full glory reflected now shines on the stream;

'Tis the star-spangled banner; O long may it wave

O'er the land of the free, and the home of the brave!

And where is that band who so vauntingly swore

That the havoc of war and the battle's confusion

A home and a country should leave us no more?

Their blood has washed out their foul footsteps, pollution.

No refuge could save the hireling and slave

From the terror of flight, or the gloom
of the grave;

And the star-spangled banner in
triumph doth wave

O'er the land of the free, and the home
of the brave.

O! thus be it ever, when freemen shall stand

Between their loved homes and the war's desolation!

Blest with victory and peace, may the heav'n-rescued land

Praise the power that hath made and preserved us a nation.

Then conquer we must, for our cause it is just,

And this be our motto—"In God is our trust":

And the star-spangled banner in triumph shall wave

O'er the land of the free, and the home of the brave.

-Francis Scott Key

Lesson 31: Read the poem and complete the copywork that follows in your best handwriting.

Father William

"You are old, Father William," the young man said,
"And your hair has become very white;
And yet you incessantly stand on your head—
Do you think, at your age, it is right?"
"In my youth," Father William replied to his son,
"I feared it might injure the brain;
But now that I'm perfectly sure I have none,
Why, I do it again and again."
"You are old," said the youth, "as I mentioned before,
And have grown most uncommonly fat;
Yet you turned a back-somersault in at the door—
Pray, what is the reason of that?"
"In my youth," said the sage, as he shook his gray locks,
"I kept all my limbs very supple
By the use of this ointment—one shilling the box—
Allow me to sell you a couple."
"You are old," said the youth, "and your jaws are too weak
For anything tougher than suet;
Yet you finished the goose, with the bones and the beak:
Pray, how did you manage to do it?"
"In my youth," said his father, "I took to the law,
And argued each case with my wife;
And the muscular strength which it gave to my jaw
Has lasted the rest of my life."
"You are old," said the youth; "one would hardly suppose
That your eye was as steady as ever;
Yet you balanced an eel on the end of your nose—
What made you so awfully clever?"
"I have answered three questions, and that is enough,"
Said his father, "don't give yourself airs!
Do you think I can listen all day to such stuff?
Be off, or I'll kick you down-stairs!"
-Lewis Carroll

Father William

"You are old, Father William," the young man said,

"And your hair has become very white;

And yet you incessantly stand on your head—

Do you think, at your age, it is
right?"

"In my youth," Father William
replied to his son,

"I feared it might injure the brain;

But now that I'm perfectly sure I
have none,

Why, I do it again and again."

"You are old," said the youth, "as I mentioned before,

And have grown most uncommonly fat;

Yet you turned a back-somersault in at the door—

Pray, what is the reason of that?"

"In my youth," said the sage, as he shook his gray locks,

"I kept all my limbs very supple

By the use of this ointment—one shilling the box—

Allow me to sell you a couple."

"You are old," said the youth, "and your jaws are too weak

For anything tougher than suet;

Yet you finished the goose, with the bones and the beak:

Pray, how did you manage to do it?"

"In my youth," said his father, "I
took to the law,

And argued each case with my wife;

And the muscular strength which it
gave to my jaw

Has lasted the rest of my life."

"You are old," said the youth; "one would hardly suppose

That your eye was as steady as ever;

Yet you balanced an eel on the end of your nose—

What made you so awfully clever?"

"I have answered three questions, and that is enough,"

Said his father, "don't give yourself airs!

Do you think I can listen all day to such stuff?

Be off, or I'll kick you down-stairs!"

-Lewis Carroll

Lesson 32: Read the poem and complete the copywork that follows in your best handwriting.

The Nightingale and the Glow-worm
A nightingale, that all day long
Had cheered the village with his song,
Nor yet at eve his note suspended,
Nor yet when eventide was ended,
Began to feel, as well he might,
The keen demands of appetite;
When, looking eagerly around,
He spied far off, upon the ground,
A something shining in the dark,
And knew the glow-worm by his spark;
So, stooping down from hawthorn top,
He thought to put him in his crop.
The worm, aware of his intent,
Harangued him thus, right eloquent:
"Did you admire my lamp," quoth he,
"As much as I your minstrelsy,
You would abhor to do me wrong,
As much as I to spoil your song;
For 'twas the self-same power divine,
Taught you to sing and me to shine;
That you with music, I with light,
Might beautify and cheer the night."
The songster heard his short oration,
And warbling out his approbation,
Released him, as my story tells,
And found a supper somewhere else.
-William Cowper

The Nightingale and the Glow-worm

A nightingale, that all day long

Had cheered the village with his song,

Nor yet at eve his note suspended,

Nor yet when eventide was ended,

Began to feel, as well he might,

The keen demands of appetite;

When, looking eagerly around,

He spied far off, upon the ground,

A something shining in the dark,

And knew the glow-worm by his spark;

So, stooping down from hawthorn top,

He thought to put him in his crop.

The worm, aware of his intent,

Harangued him thus, right eloquent:

"Did you admire my lamp," quoth he,

"As much as I your minstrelsy,

You would abhor to do me wrong,

As much as I to spoil your song;

For 'twas the self-same power divine,

Taught you to sing and me to shine;

That you with music, I with light,

Might beautify and cheer the night."

The songster heard his short oration,

And warbling out his approbation,

Released him, as my story tells,

And found a supper somewhere else.

-William Cowper

Made in the USA
Monee, IL
12 April 2022

94641347R10103